Holiday Cheer
Brain Teasers

————— • —————

by

S. Claus

RED-LETTER PRESS, INC.
Saddle River, New Jersey

HOLIDAY CHEER BRAIN TEASERS
COPYRIGHT ©2014 Red-Letter Press, Inc.
ISBN-13: 978-1-60387-092-4
ISBN: 1-60387-092-X

Red-Letter Press, Inc.
P.O. Box 393
Saddle River, NJ 07458

www.Red-LetterPress.com

ACKNOWLEDGMENTS

EDITORIAL:
Jack Kreismer

•

BOOK DESIGN & TYPOGRAPHY:
Jeff Kreismer

•

COVER & INTERIOR ART:
Andrew Towl

•

RESEARCH & DEVELOPMENT:
Russ Edwards
Kobus Reyneke

•

CONTRIBUTORS:
Jim Tomlinson
Rory Tomlinson

Holiday Cheer
Brain Teasers

SEASONAL STUMPER

As you're beginning to tackle the brain teasers in this book, Santa's already begun to wind down from another trip around the world, having racked up tens of thousands of miles with his reindeer buddies.

Speaking of mileage, Santa's personal station wagon had certainly seen better days so as soon as he got back to the North Pole he bought a shiny new red one as bright as Rudolph's nose.

On the way home to tell Mrs. Claus about his purchase, Santa went the wrong way up Mistletoe Lane, a one-way street. He bumped into Jingles the elf, nearly knocking him over, then went up onto the sidewalk for a bit before deciding to take a shortcut right over the North Pole skating pond. A policeman from North Pole's finest was watching Santa's eventful trip the whole time, yet he did not arrest him. How come?

HOSPITAL FOR THE HEALTHY

Waldo spent a couple of days in the hospital even though he wasn't sick or injured. In fact, physically there was absolutely nothing wrong with him, yet when it came time for him to leave, it was necessary for Waldo to be carried out. How come?

Answer (Seasonal Stumper)

Santa was walking.

Answer (Hospital for the Healthy)

Waldo was a two-day old baby.

 What is it that, the more you take, the more you leave behind?

Footsteps

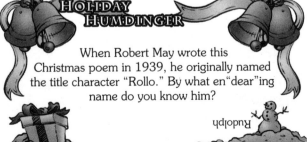

HOLIDAY HUMDINGER

When Robert May wrote this Christmas poem in 1939, he originally named the title character "Rollo." By what en"dear"ing name do you know him?

Rudolph

POP QUIZ

Let's see if you have a head for numbers. For an extra slice of fruitcake this Christmas, do the following straightforward multiplication problem in your head in just one minute. If you can't, you get TWO extra slices of fruitcake!

$$68 \times 3 \times 10 \times 2 \times 0 \times 5 \times 2$$

PING PONG PROBLEM

You're proud of your finished basement and your new rec room. The construction is nearly finished when you invite your buddies over for a ping-pong match. The play is fast and furious all evening long and you are down to the game that will determine the winner. Then, disaster strikes!

Your last usable ping-pong ball bounces down a narrow pipe embedded in concrete in the basement floor left over from the construction. The only tools you have at hand are a tape measure, a blowtorch, a nail gun, your bottle of drinking water, a drinking straw, two 9-Volt batteries, a pack of chewing gum, a tire patch kit, a length of twine, a bar of soap and a pair of pliers. How would you manage to retrieve the ball undamaged so you could get back to your game?

Answer (Pop Quiz)

0 – Any number or series of numbers multiplied
by 0 is 0. Make sure your dental insurance is paid up
and get out that fruitcake!

Answer (Ping Pong Problem)

You uncap your drinking water and pour it
down the pipe. The ball will float to the top.
Dry it off and you're ready to serve.

 *In the United States of America, it's a
known fact that the majority of
buildings do not have a 13th floor.
How come?*

They're not tall enough.

HOLIDAY HUMDINGER

Who wrote *The Gift of the Magi?*

O. Henry

Touching Base

tI saw no enuJ 32, 3691, ta eht oloP sdnuorG nehw
ynaz steM redleifretnec ymmiJ llasreiP tfel sih tsom
elbaromem noisserpmi no weN kroY. llasreiP dah a
71-raey gib eugael reerac dekram yb eno lufroloc
tnedicni retfa rehtona. eH ecno deppets pu ot eht
etalp gniraew a seltaeB giw elihw gniyalp "ria
ratiug" no sih tab, del sreehc rof flesmih ni eht
dleiftuo gnirud skaerb ni yalp, dna dih dniheb eht
stnemunom ta eht dlo eeknaY muidatS dna
"deklat" ot ebaB htuR. tuB sih erutangis emag
emac no taht enuJ noonretfa, eht renepo fo a
redaehelbuod tsniaga eht aihpledalihP seillihP.
weN s'kroY lraC yelliW dehctip a tnaillirb 0-5
tuotuhs; revewoh llasreiP saw eht klat fo eht nwot,
ton os hcum rof sih enotselim remoh, tub rof tahw
eh did ot etaromemmoc ti. gnicaF aihpledalihP
rehctip sallaD neerG, llasreiP detfol a pop ylf revo
eht thgir-dleif ecnef rof eht ht001 emoh nur fo sih
reerac. tahW dewollof, emos deredisnoc ot eb
suoiralih. srehtO deredisnoc ti enasni. eugaeL
slaiciffo erew ton desuma. A yad retal, a gnilur saw
deussi ot tibihorp siht dnik fo roivaheb. fI ev'uoy
daer siht raf, uoy nac ylbaborp sseug tahw ti saw
taht llasreiP did ot etarbelec eht noisacco. t'naC
uoy?

Answer (Touching Base)

He ran the bases backwards!

 You're the bus driver. At the first stop, 4 people get on. At the second stop, 8 people get on. At the third stop, 2 people get off. Finally, at the fourth stop, the remaining passengers get off. The question is– What color are the bus driver's eyes?

The same as yours– You're the bus driver.

HOLIDAY HUMDINGER

Kevin McCallister is the lead character in what two popular Christmas flicks?

Home Alone and Home Alone 2: Lost in New York (He's portrayed by Macaulay Culkin.)

PENGUIN PUZZLER

Quinn the Eskimo was quite the hunter. He was pretty good at shooting off at the mouth, too. Not only would he tell you about his latest conquest; he'd tell you every little detail about the critter he bagged. That's just what he was doing at the local tavern one cold, wintry North Pole night.

"I'm tellin' you, Sal," Quinn said to the bartender, "I nabbed me an emperor penguin- had to be around 90 lbs. That's as big as they come. You know, them penguins are the only birds that can swim, but can't fly," said the Eskimo, explaining his catch while all the while demonstrating detailed knowledge of his prey.

"Oh, yeah," said Sal, visibly unimpressed.

"That's right," the Eskimo replied. "And this one was in the water when I got 'im. He was in a colony. That's what they call a group of penguins, ya know."

"Yeah, I know- I know a thing or two about penguins, too," said Sal. "And I know you didn't catch one."

Sal was right. Quinn wasn't only shooting off at the mouth- he put his foot in it this time. Can you explain?

Answer (Penguin Puzzler)

Quinn the Eskimo lives at the North Pole.
Penguins live in the Southern Hemisphere.

 *A guy is sentenced to a cruel death.
He has to pick one of three rooms
to meet his fate. Room #1 is a fiery
inferno. In room #2, there are ten
assassins with loaded guns. Room #3
houses a dozen lions that weren't fed
for six months. Which room should he
choose?*

Room #3– The lions would be dead if they
hadn't eaten in six months.

HOLIDAY HUMDINGER

According to the hit song,
what is always number one on
Alvin the Chipmunk's Christmas list?

A hula-hoop

From Bad to Verse

1. There is in English a word that almost certainly confounds, because in the space of just five letters it contains four personal pronouns. What is it?

2. Hard to answer, easy to prove, what goes up and down but doesn't move?

3. I have four fingers and a thumb, but flesh and bone I have none. What am I?

4. 'Tis used between your head and toes, the more it works the thinner it grows. What is it?

Sign Language

Are you a "roads scholar"? If so, there should be no trouble in spotting what's wrong with these interstate highway signs...

I-98 South

I-47 West

I-82 North

Answers (From Bad to Verse)

1. Usher (us, she, he, her)

2. The temperature

3. A glove

4. Soap

Answer (Sign Language)

Interstate highways running north-south have odd numbers and have even numbers if running east-west.

 Name the most recent year in which New Year's came before Christmas.

This year. New Year's always comes before Christmas of the same year.

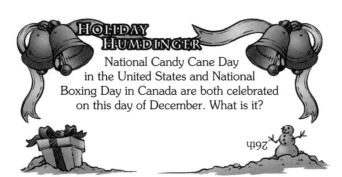

HOLIDAY HUMDINGER

National Candy Cane Day in the United States and National Boxing Day in Canada are both celebrated on this day of December. What is it?

26th

Tom Swifties

The adverb makes the pun here. Example: "I won't use that electric saw again- it's too dangerous," Tom said **offhandedly**. "See how many of the following Tom Swifties you can fill in," we say **blankly**.

1. "You have the right to remain silent," Tom said _____.

2. "I just struck oil," Tom _____.

3. "I'm going to wear a ribbon around my arm," Tom said with _____.

4. "I've gone and dropped my toothpaste," said Tom _____.

5. "I came in through the main door," said Tom _____.

6. "On the beach, the only thing you can count on is the sea spray," Tom said _____.

7. "I really enjoy condiments made with chopped up pickles," Tom said with _____.

8. "I've heard that the Octomom wants more children," Tom said _____.

9. "It turns out that for all his money Donald actually WANTS his hair like that," Tom _____.

10. "I admit that I always have trouble being on time," Tom said _____.

Answers (Tom Swifties)

1. arrestingly

2. gushed

3. abandon

4. crestfallen

5. entranced

6. mistrustfully

7. relish

8. kiddingly

9. trumpeted

10. belatedly

HOLIDAY HUMDINGER

While now revered, this Christmas spirit was outlawed in England by Oliver Cromwell between 1649 and 1660.

Christmas carols

STATING THE FACTS

Ten statements follow below.
How many in this quiz are true?

1. There is one false statement.

2. There are two false statements.

3. There are three false statements.

4. There are four false statements.

5. There are five false statements.

6. There are six false statements.

7. There are seven false statements.

8. There are eight false statements.

9. There are nine false statements.

10. There are ten false statements.

RHYME TIME

Until I am measured
I am not known.
Yet how you miss me
When I have flown.
What am I?

Answer (Stating the Facts)

Two- Number 9 is a true statement because 1 through 8 and 10 are false. The very first sentence of the quiz-"Ten statements follow below." –is also true.

Answer (Rhyme Time)

Time

 Which are bigger, a peacock's eggs or a chicken's eggs?

Chicken eggs are infinitely bigger, especially since there's no such thing as a peacock egg. A female peacock is a peahen.

HOLIDAY HUMDINGER

In the poem *The Night Before Christmas*, how many times is Santa's name mentioned?

0

WOMEN'S INTUITION

1. Welcome to the mysterious Madame Claus' Parlor of Psychic Power...

Please, pick a number.
Now, double it...
Add 10...
Subtract 4...
Add 2...
Divide it in half...
Take away the number you first thought of...

...I see in my ice crystal ball that the answer is four.

2. To further prove Santa isn't the only one who knows all about you, I have taken your age in years, multiplied it by 99 and added the digits in the answer together. Hmm...let's see.

I get 18. How about you?

PURR-PLEXING

A well-dressed fellow parks his car, gets out, makes sure all the doors and windows are locked, and even checks to make certain that the trunk is not open. He goes about his business and when he returns a few minutes later, he finds a cat nestled up fast asleep on the back seat. How did the cat manage to get into the car?

Answers (Women's Intuition)

Thank you very much...Pay the elf on the way out.
Some secrets you keep to yourself, sweetheart.

Answer (Purr-plexing)

It was a convertible.

 Taking all the numbers between 1 and 1 million, in what scenario would 8 be the first and 2202 be the last number?

If the numbers were arranged in alphabetical order, eight would come first and two thousand two hundred and two would be last.

HOLIDAY HUMDINGER

Charles W. Howard founded this institution in Midland, Michigan, in 1937. It is the longest continuously running school of its kind in the world. What do people learn there?

How to be Santa- It's official name is the Charles W. Howard Santa Claus School.

BASEBALL BAFFLER

Step up to the plate and see if you can handle this
hardball teaser that actually occurred.

Nolan Ryan... Bob Feller... Justin Verlander...
Give them their due with their 100 mph
heaters, but they couldn't hold a candle to the
flame-throwing of Hayden Siddhartha "Sidd" Finch
according to *Sports Illustrated's* April 1, 1985
cover story.

The magazine reported that the 28-year-old
eccentric rookie from Tibet had been blowing away
the Mets coaching staff during spring training with
far and away the fastest fastball anyone had ever
seen- an amazing 168 miles per hour.

So why was it, then, that Finch's name made
an equally quick disappearance from the sports
pages?

A FAMILIAR FACE

Cornelius was vacationing at Disney World when
he ran into his long lost uncle. He disappeared
from the family before Cornelius was even born.
Cornelius had never met nor even seen him, not
even in a picture. Nonetheless, Cornelius easily
recognized his uncle. How come?

Answer (Baseball Baffler)

Note the date of the issue, April 1- It was an
April Fool's joke by the publication.

Answer (A Familiar Face)

Cornelius' uncle was his dad's identical twin.

 *What do vets and dog lovers alike
usually call little dogs with
white-colored coats that are
sometimes curly-haired and other
times spotted, sometimes long-tailed
and other times not?*

Puppies

HOLIDAY HUMDINGER

Name the precision dance
company that was founded in St. Louis,
Missouri, by Russell Markert in 1925 and
performs annually at the Radio City Christmas
Spectacular in New York City.

The Rockettes

Music To Your Ears

Mrs. Claus loves to sing holiday songs. Can you identify the following song titles from the first letter of each word?

1. A I W F C I M T F T

2. R T R-N R

3. I S M K S C

4. T T D O C

5. H! T H A S

6. O L T O B

Traveling Troubles

You are driving in a car at a constant speed. On your left hand side there is a valley. On your right, Santa's traveling on his sleigh at the same speed as you. In front of you, there is a rhinoceros on the run. Behind you there is a helicopter flying at ground level. Both the rhino and the helicopter are traveling at the exact same same speed as you. What must you do to safely maneuver out of this highly dangerous situation?

Answers (Music To Your Ears)

1. *All I Want For Christmas Is My Two Front Teeth*

2. *Rudolph the Red-Nosed Reindeer*

3. *I Saw Mommy Kissing Santa Claus*

4. *The Twelve Days of Christmas*

5. *Hark! The Herald Angels Sing*

6. *O' Little Town of Bethlehem*

Answer (Traveling Troubles)

Get off the merry-go-round - you've had
way too much eggnog.

HOLIDAY HUMDINGER

What did Frank Borman,
James Lovell and William Anders
circle 10 times on Christmas Eve in 1968?

The Moon- They were the Apollo 8
astronauts who were the first to
accomplish a lunar orbital flight.

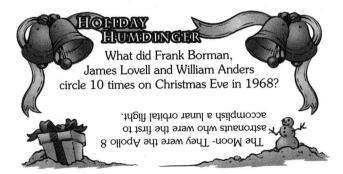

TRIVIAL TWOFERS

Here, you have two cracks at the same answer- Answer the trivia question and you also have the solution to the numerical teaser below it. Conversely, if you can figure out the sequentially proper number to fill in the blank, you've got the trivia question answered, too.

1. How many dominoes are in a standard set?
43, 38, 34, 31, 29, __

2. What's the weight, in pounds, of a men's "shot" in the shot put?
2, 4, __, 256, 65,536, 4,294,967,296

3. What's the only number with its letters in reverse alphabetical order?
_, 11, 21, 31, 21, 11, 1

4. How many flavors of ice cream are in that famous Baskin-Robbins slogan?
J 31, F 28, M __, A 30, M 31, J 30

5. How many nephews does Popeye have?
T, N, E, S, S, F, _, T, T, O

6. In a perfect game in baseball, how many batters does a pitcher face?
3, 9, __, 51, 153, 459

7. How many states in the U.S. begin with the letter "M"?
S6, M6, T7, W9, T_, F6, S8

Answers (Trivial Twofers)

1. 28- Numbers are subtracted sequentially: 43 – 5, 38 – 4, etc.

2. 16- The numbers are squared: 2 x 2 = 4, 4 x 4 = 16, etc.

3. 1- The numbers are a palindrome- they read the same forward and backward.

4. 31- Starting with January, the letters designate the months of the year and the numbers are the amount of days in that month.

5. 4- Pipeye, Peepeye, Pupeye, and Poopeye...
The letters represent the first letter of numbers in the countdown from 10 to 1.

6. 27- The numbers are in sequential multiplications of 3: 3 x 3 = 9 x 3 = 27, etc.

7. 8- Maine, Maryland, Massachusetts, Michigan, Minnesota, Mississippi, Missouri, and Montana...The numbers correspond to the amount of letters in each day of the week: S (for Sunday) 6; M (for Monday) 6; etc.

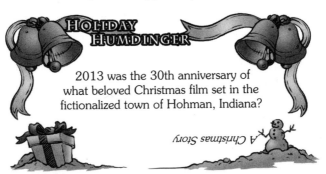

HOLIDAY HUMDINGER

2013 was the 30th anniversary of what beloved Christmas film set in the fictionalized town of Hohman, Indiana?

A Christmas Story

GARBLEDEGOOKS

Unscramble the letters below to find
things associated with Christmas.

1. oty rtisna

2. ttmsieleo

3. otdcenisora

4. snitel

5. oarcls

6. ehtre swei nme

7. skwidlea natass

8. hte atnrkrceuc

9. tcrhsisam retes

10. skoctgins

HUNTING FOR AN ANSWER?

Jack shot not one, not two, but three- count 'em
- three eagles on that crisp autumn afternoon!
Though he knew his wife wouldn't be particularly
proud of what he'd done, his buddies were in awe
of the achievement- shooting three eagles without
killing a single one. How is that possible?

Answers (Garbledegooks)

1. Toy trains

2. Mistletoe

3. Decorations

4. Tinsel

5. Carols

6. Three Wise Men

7. Sidewalk Santa

8. The Nutcracker

9. Christmas trees

10. Stockings

Answer (Hunting For An Answer?)

He eagled three holes in a round of golf.

HOLIDAY HUMDINGER

At what point in the holiday season does "Cyber Monday" fall?

It is the Monday following "Black Friday", which follows Thanksgiving. Cyber Monday is the busiest online shopping day of the year.

FATHER OF INVENTION

Simpson S. Skinner, the mad inventor, rushed into the patent office with a test tube full of green liquid. "I want to patent my new invention immediately!" he demanded. "Before someone else steals it."

"What is it?" asked the bored patent examiner.

"I have it here," answered Skinner, holding up the test tube. "It's the world's most powerful acid. It will eat through anything."

"Take a seat," said the examiner. "Don't worry, no one will steal your idea."

How did he know?

RHYME TIME

Heart of Darkness,
Coat of Grain,
I was once alive,
Now feel no pain.
I never walk, but
Leave a Trail,
Circle head and pointed tail.
I grow shorter as the day goes on,
My waistline is a hexagon.
What am I?

Answer (Father of Invention)

Because it didn't work... If it ate through anything, how could Skinner keep it in the test tube?

Answer (Rhyme Time)

A pencil

 Happy, Sleepy, Dopey, Doc, Grumpy, Sneezy and Bashful make up the Seven Dwarfs. Who was the tallest in the Seven Dwarfs' household?

Snow White

HOLIDAY HUMDINGER

What Christmas song contains the line, "I've brought some corn for popping"?

Let It Snow

CRYPTO-CAROLS

See if you can decipher the first line of these well-known
Christmas songs by figuring out what letters to
substitute. (Each title uses a different solution.)

1. J BJAN FGG LN ZFHRQZVG

2. BR XOMLRBTS FY L DPBQM UPOBAQRLA

3. RPTYSQ DQSSC RPTYSQ DQSSC RPTYSQ
   FSS MAQ HFE

PEERING PIRATES

"Arrgh, me mateys," croaked the buccaneer as he
settled in for some grog and a bit o' tale tellin'.

"I remember it like yesterday," he said, taking a
sip. "By Blackbeard's ghost I swear it was as fine
a day of sailin' as anyone ever did see. There we
were, a sleek ship and a scurvy crew just passing
the spice isle of Madagascar and making for the
Maldives, rich in rum and women. My first mate
stood on the poop deck and faced east while my
second mate stood on the same deck and faced
west, and on my oath, it was so clear they could
see each other."

How is it possible the old pirate was telling the
truth?

Answers (Crypto-Carols)

1. O Come All Ye Faithful

2. I'm Dreaming of a White Christmas

3. Jingle Bells, Jingle Bells, Jingle All the Way

Answer (Peering Pirates)

The first mate stood on the west side and faced east while the second mate stood on the east side and faced west. They were only a few feet from each other.

A deaf man wanted to buy a buzz-saw at a hardware store. How would he indicate that to the salesperson?

He'd say, "I would like to buy a buzz-saw."

HOLIDAY HUMDINGER

What President banned Christmas trees from the White House in 1912?

Teddy Roosevelt, because of his strong environmental concerns

Loco-Motion

What mode of transportation do the following refer to?

1. This popular way of getting around is one almost any can afford. But strangely, while there are eight wheels on the ground, there's only room for one on board.

2. Up here at Santa's workshop, most visitors come by sleigh and a few arrive by plane or helicopter. What's the only way to visit the North Pole without flying or traveling over the snow?

Horseplay

1. A man riding on horseback left from New York for San Francisco on Tuesday and arrived on the very same Tuesday. How can this be?

2. A horse is tied to a 15-foot rope and a bale of hay is 25 feet away. How is it that the horse is able to eat that hay?

Score Unsure

What's the one sport where neither the spectators nor participants know who is winning until the very end?

Answers (Loco-Motion)

1. Roller skates

2. Submarine – The North Pole is in the middle of the ocean.

Answers (Horse Play)

1. The horse's name was Tuesday.

2. He simply walks over and eats it. The horse may be tied to the rope, but the rope isn't tied to anything!

Answer (Score Unsure)

Boxing

Christmas Island is considered
a territory of what nation?

Australia

COMMON NAMES

Santa's subordinate clauses have put together this elfish quiz for you. Try to find the common word that fits with the other three.

Example: Jingle, Silver, Sleigh
Answer: Bells

1. Bunk, Room, Twin

2. Place, Fly, Grease

3. Movie, Desk, Price

4. Elevator, Mine, Drive

5. Christmas, Shoe, Family

6. Flash, Business, Place

7. Show, Big, Computer

8. Tense, Christmas, Company

9. Ice, Sky, Paint

10. Fog, River, Account

Answers (Common Names)

1. Bed

2. Fire

3. Set

4. Shaft

5. Tree

6. Card

7. Game

8. Present

9. Scraper

10. Bank

HOLIDAY HUMDINGER

While it took almost 50 years
for the idea to catch on, J.W. Parkinson's
Department Store in Philadelphia featured the
first one of these in 1841.

A departments store Santa

A FRIENDLY ENCOUNTER

Trixie was shopping at Toys For Boys when she ran into an old friend.

"Oh, I see you have a family now," Trixie said as she smiled at her friend's little boy.

"Yes, I got married 8 years ago. Hey, we should get together sometime. I'd love for you to meet my significant other."

Trixie said, "That would be nice. Say, what's your son's name?"

"It's the same as Daddy's," replied her friend.

"Well, hello Eddie. It's nice to meet you."

How did Trixie know the boy's name?

RHYME TIME

I'll never be seen, no matter how bold.
You can capture me, but don't try to hold.
I have no throat and can't say a word,
But when I'm around I can often be heard.
What am I?

Answer (A Friendly Encounter)

Trixie's friend was a guy.

Answer (Rhyme Time)

The wind

 A man pushed and pushed his car past various hotels. He stopped when he reached a certain hotel and realized he was bankrupt. Why?

He was playing Monopoly.

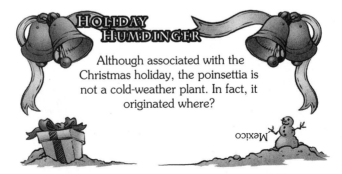

HOLIDAY HUMDINGER

Although associated with the Christmas holiday, the poinsettia is not a cold-weather plant. In fact, it originated where?

Mexico

INITIALLY SPEAKING

In this quiz, the number on the left is based upon the first letters for words which are provided on the right.

Example: 4 = Q. in a G.
Answer: Quarts in a Gallon

1. 26 = L. in the A.

2. 54 = C. in the D. (with the J.)

3. 12 = S. of the Z.

4. 20,000 = L. U. the S.

5. 13 = O.C.

6. 18 = H. on a G. C.

7. 206 = B. in the H. B.

8. 8 = S. on an O.

9. 101 = D.

10. 9 = S. C.'s R. (including R.)

Answers (Initially Speaking)

1. 26 = Letters in the Alphabet

2. 54 = Cards in the Deck (with the Jokers)

3. 12 = Signs of the Zodiac

4. 20,000 = Leagues Under the Sea

5. 13 = Original Colonies

6. 18 = Holes on a Golf Course

7. 206 = Bones in the Human Body

8. 8 = Sides on an Octagon

9. 101 = Dalmatians

10. 9 = Santa Claus' Reindeer (including Rudolph)

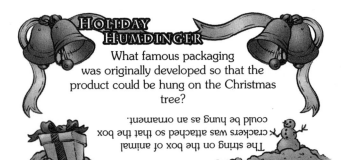

HOLIDAY HUMDINGER
What famous packaging was originally developed so that the product could be hung on the Christmas tree?

The string on the box of animal crackers was attached so that the box could be hung as an ornament.

BLANKETY-BLANKS

The two blanks in each sentence can be
filled in with a pair of anagrams.

**Example: "Please _____ the poem to me, _____,"
said Santa to Mrs. Claus.**
Answer: read, dear

1. Mrs. Claus said to her _____, "That's a fine _____
of reindeer you have for your journey."

2. Even though she was so _____, Mrs. Claus _____
to remain awake on Christmas Eve until Santa
came home.

3. Santa and his team _____ the world to make
certain no child is _____looked on Christmas Eve.

4. It was almost time for Santa to leave on his trek
so the elves ran around looking for a _____ of the
_____ filled with toys.

5. _____ for the naughty children, all youngsters
should _____ a stocking filled with toys.

6. Thank heavens the _____ didn't rust the _____
runners on Santa's sleigh.

7. If the manufacturer's _____ is not in the box
when you open it, don't _____ the customer service
rep when you return the gift to the store.

Answers (Blankety Blank)

1. Mate, team

2. Tired, tried

3. Rove, over

4. Trace, crate

5. Except, expect

6. Sleet, steel

7. Rebate, berate

This real life teaser occurred in 1940. Hall of Fame pitcher Bob Feller threw a no-hitter for the Cleveland Indians against the Chicago White Sox, yet none of the opposing players batting averages changed. How come?

It was Opening Day.

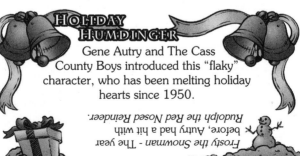

HOLIDAY HUMDINGER
Gene Autry and The Cass County Boys introduced this "flaky" character, who has been melting holiday hearts since 1950.

Frosty the Snowman - The year before, Autry had a hit with *Rudolph the Red Nosed Reindeer.*

PHRASE CRAZE

Here are some trivial messages that Santa's elves have scrawled on the workshop windows for you to solve.

Example: EGGS   is eggs over easy.
         EASY

1. FRIENDJUSTFRIEND

2. ALL world

3. SYMPHON

4. O_ER_T_O_

5. AOBLNUECMOEON

6. 10SNE1

7. AGB

8. AMᑌOUS

9. THEFREDACE

10. DNA4TH

11. LITTLE LITTLE
    LATE LATE

12. TIMING   TIM ING

Answers (Phrase Craze)

1. Just between friends

2. It's a small world after all.

3. Unfinished symphony

4. Painless operation

5. Once in a blue moon

6. Tennis, anyone?

7. Mixed bag

8. Ambiguous

9. Red in the face

10. Back and forth

11. Too little, too late

12. Split second timing

HOLIDAY HUMDINGER

In 1958, what 13-year-old recorded
Rockin' Around the Christmas Tree?

Brenda Lee

LAZING SADDLES

On this installment of Brainteasers of the Old West, we find aging cattle baron Chet Masterson talking to his two sons.

"Boys, I'm a headin' for the last roundup," he said as he knocked back a whiskey to wash the taste of the cigar out of his mouth. "I've pondered long and hard who to leave my vast fortune to. Nigh onto half the steers in Texas are under my brand and I've decided to leave it all to the winner of a horse race. Only this ain't no ordinary race, no siree! The one with the slowest horse gets to be the big he-bull around here. All the other one gets is my silver plated spittoon."

The rules of the contest required the boys to ride to the Texas border and then "race" back to the ranch house. At the starting pistol, each tried to ride slower than the other. After five days in the hot West Texas sun, they still found themselves wandering aimlessly around the desert. After they had passed his place for the twentieth time, an old sodbuster waved them over and asked them what in tarnation was going on. They explained everything to him, whereupon he thought for a moment and said something to the boys. Hearing this, they both took off at a full gallop towards home.

What did the old sodbuster say?

Answer (Lazing Saddles)

He told them to switch horses.

Seven pieces of coal, a carrot and a scarf are lying on little Johnny's front yard. No one, including Johnny, had put them on the lawn yet there's a plausible reason why they should be there. Do you know it?

Johnny had made a snowman and, eventually, it melted.

Fill in the missing name:
"Yes, _____, there is a Santa Claus."

Virginia

BY THE NUMBERS

1. What is the only case where half of 5 is 4?

2. There are 52 cards in a deck...Ace, two, three, four, five, six, seven, eight, nine, ten, jack, queen and king. What odd coincidence do you notice about these words?

3. If you wrote down all the numbers from 1 to 100, how many times would the digit 9 appear?

4. You have two plastic jugs filled with water. One is a gallon and one is a half gallon. You have to transfer the water into a wooden barrel, but you want to know afterwards which water came from which jug. Is there any way to do this?

RHYME TIME

Although liquid splashes me,
None seeps through.
Protecting things is what I do.
Of colors, I come in quite a range.
When I'm hit, my hue will change.
What am I?

Answers (By The Numbers)

1. Half of FIVE is "IV", the Roman numeral for four.

2. The names spelled out have exactly 52 letters!

3. 20 (including 90, 91, etc.)

4. Yes – Freeze the water, cut away the jugs and keep the barrel cold!

Answer (Rhyme Time)

Skin

How can a man go eight days without sleeping?

He sleeps at night.

Who did the first recording of *Here Comes Santa Claus?*

Gene Autry

SINGING A SONG FOR SIXPENCE

Warren Smorgasbord, the fabulously wealthy but socially conscious entrepreneur, found himself sitting next to a scruffily dressed beach bum type at a Tiki bar in Honolulu. The two struck up a conversation and Smorgasbord asked the man what he did for a living. The man claimed that he had a unique talent. He knew every song ever written, and if you gave him a lady's name, he would sing you an actual song with that name in it. He guaranteed that the song would be verifiable no matter how long the name.

"Well, I'm a betting man," said Smorgasbord. "Tell you what. I'll bet whatever's in my wallet against one of those flaming Rum Wiki Wacky Waikiki drinks that I can give you a name that you can't come up with a song for. In fact, it's my daughter's- Maria Kathryn Elizabeth Ethel Conchata, Evelyn Rebecca Suzette Smorgasbord-Von Hindenbacker."

Quite a challenge on the surface, but the beach bum went home with a well-stuffed wallet and Smorgasbord went home several thousand dollars wiser.

How did the beachcomber win the bet?

Answer (Song for Sixpence)

He simply sang *Happy Birthday* with
the young lady's name in it.

*A monkey, a squirrel, and a bird are
racing to the top of a coconut tree.
Who will get the banana first—
the monkey, the squirrel or the bird?*

None of them— You can't get a
banana from a coconut tree.

HOLIDAY HUMDINGER

What two Muppets got their
names from characters in
It's A Wonderful Life?

Bert and Ernie

LAUGH-IN TIME-OUT

It's time for a teaser break from one of Santa's favorite blasts from the past. Say two words- "no respect" –and you think of one comedian, Rodney Dangerfield. Now see if you can fill in two words to complete these one-liners from the king of self-deprecation.

1. What a childhood I had. Why, when I took my first step, my old man _ _ _ _ _ _ _ _ _.

2. I asked my old man if I could go ice-skating on the lake. He said, "Wait til it _ _ _ _ _ _ _ _ _ _."

3. I remember the time I was kidnapped and they sent back a piece of my finger to my father. He said he wanted _ _ _ _ _ _ _ _ _.

4. My uncle's dying wish was to have me sitting on his lap. He was in the _ _ _ _ _ _ _ _ _ _ _ _ _.

5. A hooker once told me she had _ _ _ _ _ _ _ _ _.

6. I met the surgeon general. He offered me _

   _ _ _ _ _ _ _ _ _.

7. When I was born, the doctor took one look at my face, turned me over and said, "_ _ _ _,

   _ _ _ _ _!"

Answers (Remembering Rodney)

1. tripped me

2. gets warmer

3. more proof

4. electric chair

5. a headache

6. a cigarette

7. "Look, twins!"

 How do you walk on water?

Freeze it first.

HOLIDAY HUMDINGER

The Democratic donkey, Republican elephant and modern image of Santa Claus were all created by the same cartoonist. Who?

Thomas Nast

QUOTE, UNQUOTE

Your job is to complete the following quote by filling in the missing word. Its correlating letters can be obtained from the stage names of the funny people whose real names are listed below.

"If you don't want your dog to have bad breath, do what I do: Pour a little Lavoris in the _ _ _ _ _ _ ."
–Jay Leno

1. __ __ __ __ __ (1) __ __ __
   Birth name: Scott Thompson

2. __ (2) __ __ __ __ __ __ __ __
   Birth name: Joan Molinsky

3. __ (3) __ __ __ __
   Birth name: David Adkins

4. __ __ __ __ __ __ __ __ (4) __ __ __ __ __
   Birth name: Caryn Johnson

5. __ __ __ (5) __ __ __ __ __
   Birth name: Eric Bishop

6. __ __ __ __ __ (6) __ __ __ __ __ __ __
   __ __ __
   Birth name: Daniel Whitney

   ‾‾ ‾‾ ‾‾ ‾‾ ‾‾ ‾‾
    1   2   3   4   5   6

Answers (Quote, Unquote)

1. Scott Thompson- Carrot Top

2. Joan Molinsky- Joan Rivers

3. David Adkins- Sinbad

4. Caryn Johnson- Whoopi Goldberg

5. Eric Bishop- Jamie Foxx

6. Daniel Whitney- Larry the Cable Guy

"If you don't want your dog to have bad breath, do what I do: Pour a little Lavoris in the t o i l e t." –Jay Leno

 What's in the middle of nowhere?

The letter "h."

HOLIDAY HUMDINGER

What Christmas landmark can be found at 3159 West 11th Street in Cleveland, Ohio?

Ho Ho Ho- It's the house from the film *A Christmas Story.*

THE SCRAMBLER - RIDDLES

The answers to these groaners are all provided for you. Simply unscramble the letters and re-arrange the words... ecka a ceepi fo (a piece of cake)!

1. What does a mobster buried in cement eventually become? **dehrande a mciirlna**

2. Why did the Siamese twins move to London? **eth tohre evdir os neo lduco**

3. How do you make gold soup? **ni torarcs tpu ntereufo uyo.**

4. What happened to the employees at the struggling sardine factory? **rwee nendac teyh.**

5. The answer is: Acoustic... And the question? **lopo uyo twah od ot tohos seu?**

6. What do you get when you cross a teacher with a vampire? **dlboo tols fo ttsse**

7. Why couldn't they play cards on Noah's ark? **no tsa esucabe kdce tnpeelha eth het**

8. What would you have if all the automobiles in America were pink? **rca nkip a ntnaio**

9. Why aren't kangaroos allowed to open bank accounts? **ccskeh swlaay enucob eriht.**

10. What did one toilet say to the other? **"kolo dsluefh uyo."**

Answers (The Scrambler - Riddles)

1. A hardened criminal

2. So the other one could drive

3. You put in fourteen carrots.

4. They were canned.

5. What do you use to shoot pool?

6. Lots of blood tests

7. Because the elephant sat on the deck

8. A pink car nation

9. Their checks always bounce.

10. "You look flushed."

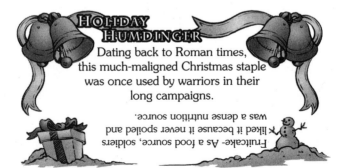

HOLIDAY HUMDINGER

Dating back to Roman times, this much-maligned Christmas staple was once used by warriors in their long campaigns.

Fruitcake- As a food source, soldiers liked it because it never spoiled and was a dense nutrition source.

CHRISTMAS TEASERS FOR YOUR INNER CHILD

1. Why does Scrooge love Rudolph the Red-Nosed Reindeer?

2. How much did Santa pay for his sleigh?

3. What do snowmen eat for breakfast?

4. What do you call a pink flamingo at the North Pole?

5. What does an electrician get for Christmas?

6. Why was Santa's little helper depressed?

7. What nationality is Santa Claus?

8. What did Adam say on the day before Christmas?

9. If athletes get athlete's foot, what do astronauts get?

10. What do you get if you deep fry Santa Claus?

Answers (Christmas Teasers)

1. Because every buck is dear to him

2. Nothing- It was on the house.

3. Frosted Flakes

4. Lost

5. Shorts

6. He had low elf-esteem.

7. North Polish

8. "It's Christmas, Eve."

9. Missiletoe

10. Crisp Cringle

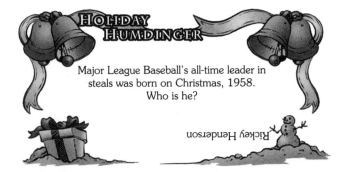

HOLIDAY HUMDINGER

Major League Baseball's all-time leader in steals was born on Christmas, 1958. Who is he?

Rickey Henderson

Weighty Business

The economy is so slow that you find yourself
working for your cousin in Jersey, affectionately
known to one and all as "Tony The Torpedo".

Now, you are not at liberty to disclose the exact
nature of your work, but let's just say that it
involves mixing cement to keep things properly
anchored in Raritan Bay.

One day, you are faced with a significant difficulty.
You find yourself needing to mix exactly five
gallons of water for enough cement for a pair of
extra large overshoes. You have plenty of water,
but you only have a 4-gallon and a 7-gallon
bucket. They're not marked off, so you can't
measure how much is in them. Now I ask you- are
these bucket manufacturers showing the proper
respect for their customers? I think not. Perhaps
Cousin Tony should pay them a visit sometime.

But I digress. Back to the water problem. You recall
we had one, er, "client" that had kicked the bucket,
and two buckets that were the wrong size. Now
how are we gonna do this job properly and leave
the vicinity before some officers of the law show up
and get the erroneous idea that we are somehow
polluting the bay?

Answer (Weighty Business)

Fill the 4-gallon bucket and dump it into the empty
7-gallon bucket. Fill the 4-gallon bucket again and
dump it into the 7-gallon bucket until it is full. Now you
have 1 gallon in the 4-gallon bucket. Empty the 7-gallon
bucket and transfer the 1 gallon from the 4-gallon bucket
into it. Now fill the 4-gallon bucket and pour it into the
7-gallon bucket and you have 5 gallons. Mix your
quick-setting cement, turn your project over to the guys
on the boat and make yourself scarce.

*What goes around the world and
stays in a corner?*

A postage stamp.

HOLIDAY HUMDINGER

If you wanted to send a letter
to Herbie the Misfit Elf, where
would you address it?

The Island of Misfit Toys, from the
Rudolph The Red-Nosed Reindeer
TV special, which has been broadcast
every year since 1964.

MINDING YOUR P'S AND Q'S

The solutions to these clues all begin with p or q.

1. It's the first name of Columbo, the television detective played by Peter Falk.

2. Y.A. Tittle was one.

3. It has 119 ridges around it.

4. Remove the last four letters of this five-letter word and it's still pronounced the same.

5. A.C. Gilbert, the inventor of the erector set, scaled new heights when he won an Olympic gold medal in 1908 in this event.

6. Mythologically, she was the first mortal woman.

7. It's the airline to Australia.

8. Leon Uris wrote this book about a British libel trial.

9. This sport bans lefties.

10. A statue honoring this naval cartoon hero stands in Crystal City, Texas.

Answers (Minding Your P's and Q's)

1. Phillip

2. A quarterback

3. A quarter

4. Queue

5. The pole vault

6. Pandora

7. Qantas

8. QBVII (which stands for Queens bench number 7, the court in which the trial takes place)

9. Polo

10. Popeye

HOLIDAY HUMDINGER

What did George Washington do on December 25, 1776?

He crossed the Delaware.

POTPOURRI

1. It gets mighty cold up here at the North Pole. One time our resident meteorologist, Spencer Christmas, reported a low temperature of minus 40 degrees. Did he mean Fahrenheit or Centigrade?

2. A man gave his wife a bottomless receptacle which was eventually used to put her flesh and blood in. Can you be more precise as to what exactly it was that he gave her?

3. We have our share of good elves and mischief-making ones. Fauntleroy is a pure delight, 100 percent honest. On the other hand, Fibber's name fits him to a tee. He can never tell the truth. One day one of them said, "The other one said he is Fibber." Which elf said that?

4. Two words that begin with the letter "g" are spelled differently, yet mean the same thing. What are they?

5. If it takes twelve elves the Twelve Days of Christmas to dig twelve holes, how long will it take one elf to dig half a hole?

Answers (Potpourri)

1. Both – That temperature is the same on both scales.

2. A wedding ring

3. It had to be Fibber. If Fauntleroy had said it, that would mean it was a true statement, thus Fibber would have been telling the truth- and he never does.

4. Gray and grey

5. A hole is a hole is a hole. There is no such thing as half a hole.

 Add three letters to make the following complete: TNESSFF_ _ _.

TTO completes the countdown from ten to one.

HOLIDAY HUMDINGER

What is the official floral emblem of Oklahoma?

Mistletoe

WHAT ARE THE ODDS?

Which is the odd one out and why?

1. a) Cocker Spaniel b) Siamese c) Boxer
   d) Golden Retriever   *Hint: Type*

2. a) New York b) Boston c) Miami
   d) San Francisco   *Hint: Location*

3. a) 2 b) 4 c) 9 d) 16   *Hint: Multiples*

4. a) *People* b) *Sports Illustrated* c) *Time*
   d) *Reader's Digest*   *Hint: Time*

5. a) pip b) radar c) mare d) peep
   Hint: Letter perfect

PAINT IT BLACK

A man dressed entirely in black is wearing a black mask covering his whole face. He stands at a crossroads in Blackville, a ghost of a town made up entirely of charcoal grey, run-down buildings. All of the streetlights are broken. There is no moon. A black-painted car without headlights drives straight toward him, but swerves in time and doesn't hit him. How did the driver avoid a collision?

Answers (What Are The Odds?)

1. B - Siamese is the only one that's not a breed of dogs.

2. D - All the other cities are on the east coast.

3. A - All the others are perfect squares.

4. D - It's the only one that's a monthly rather than a weekly periodical.

5. C - It's the only word that's not a palindrome.

Answer (Paint it Black)

It's daytime.

 What's the only thing that's eaten before it is born and after it is dead?

A chicken

HOLIDAY HUMDINGER

Santa's Little Helper is the pet Greyhound of what animated family?

The Simpsons

ONCE REMOVED

Change each pair of words into synonyms by moving one letter from one word and placing it into the other.

1. tine and bid

2. aid and scour

3. oak and west

4. potion and pierce

5. age and ranger

6. flit and croquet

7. shear and car

8. spiny and grate

9. lave and quite

10. fog and bleat

THREE CARD DRAW

Three cards are face down on the table. A Diamond is to the left of a Heart. A Five is to the right of the Jack. A King is to the left of the Spade. A Spade is to the left of the Heart. Name the three cards.

Answers (Once Removed)

1. tie and bind

2. acid and sour

3. soak and wet

4. portion and piece

5. rage and anger

6. flirt and coquet

7. sear and char

8. spin and gyrate

9. leave and quit

10. flog and beat

Answer (Three Card Draw)

King of Diamonds, Jack of Spades, Five of Hearts

HOLIDAY HUMDINGER

Ebenezer Scrooge was visited by
how many ghosts in Dickens'
A Christmas Carol?

Four- The Ghosts of Christmas
Past, Present and Yet to Come
and, of course, Jacob Marley

EASY DOES IT

Here's an obviously simple quiz with
some not so obvious answers.

1. Which can see better in total darkness - an owl,
a raccoon or a skunk?

2. What month has 28 days?

3. How many times can one be subtracted from
one hundred?

4. If your doctor gave you three pills and told you
to take one every half hour, how long would they
last?

5. A shepherd had seventeen sheep. All but seven
died. How many did he have left?

6. If you entered a dark room with only one match
and you knew that in the room there were a
kerosene lamp, an oil stove and a cigarette, which
would you light first?

7. Is there a fourth of July in England?

8. How many animals of each species did Moses
take aboard the ark?

Answers (Easy Does It)

1. No animal can see in total darkness.

2. All of them.

3. Only once.

4. One hour.

5. Seven, of course.

6. The match.

7. Yes ... There's a fourth of July everywhere.

8. None ... It was Noah who had the ark.

When you have me, you like to share me. Then again, if you share me, you don't have me. What am I?

A secret

Who, in 1856, was the first president to have a Christmas tree in the White House?

Franklin Pierce

TRAIN BRAIN DRAIN

A set of trains always conjures up Christmas memories.
Here we do our part to keep with tradition.

1. At 8 a.m. a train traveling at 70 mph leaves
Chicago for New York. At 9 a.m. a train moving at
90 mph leaves New York for Chicago. Which train
will be closer to Chicago when they meet?

2. Riley likes passenger trains but not Amtrak. He
likes the caboose but not the engine. He likes the
express but not the local, the shuttle but not the
limited. There's a dual reason for Riley's finicky
preferences. Can you explain?

3. A lightning-fast electric train is running at 100
mph in a northeasterly direction. The wind is
blowing northwesterly at 20 mph. In what direction
will the smoke from the engine blow?

4. "Toys for Boys" is a brand new shop in town
with a brand new system for selling their products.
A football costs $20; a skateboard goes for $26;
Parcheesi is $25; and a video game is $29. How
much will a train cost? (Hint: It's all in the letters.)

DRIVER'S TEST

Egbert lives in Maine. Over the next few days, he
drives to Virginia and then home to Maine. The
entire time, Egbert was driving in a northbound
lane. How come?

Answers (Train Brain Drain)

1. When they meet, they'll be the exact same distance from Chicago.

2. Riley likes words with double letters in them.

3. An electric train does not blow smoke.

4. A train will cost $13. "Toys for Boys" charges by the letters. Each consonant costs $1 and each vowel $5.

Answer (Driver's Test)

Egbert may live in Maine, but he started this trip well south of Virginia, traveled northbound through the state and then home.

You can hold it without using your hands or arms. What is it?

Your breath

HOLIDAY HUMDINGER

Who wrote *'Twas the Night Before Christmas*: Samuel Clemens or Clement C. Moore?

Clement C. Moore

FIVE EASY PIECES

The following ten letter words have been chopped up into five 2 letter chunks. See if you can re as se mb le them.

1. VE BV SI SU ER

2. SV ER AN SE TR

3. CT RY DI NA IO

4. CI TI AR AL FI

5. CC ES UL SU SF

6. IT ON IN TI IA

7. TI DI AD AL ON

8. GA ON OB TI LI

9. IB ED IN LE CR

10. NA FI ER IL NG

DAREDIVER

Elvin was an Olympic-caliber swimmer, known for his trick diving skills. Blindfolded, he leaped from a springboard into a 10-foot deep pool and didn't get wet. How did he manage this?

Answers (Five Easy Pieces)

1. Subversive

2. Transverse

3. Dictionary

4. Artificial

5. Successful

6. Initiation

7. Additional

8. Obligation

9. Incredible

10. Fingernail

Answer (Darediver)

The pool was empty.

HOLIDAY HUMDINGER

In *It's A Wonderful Life*, what did
George Bailey really want to become?

An engineer/architect

Trump Teaser

You might be thinking that even here, in *Holiday Cheer*, The Donald gets his name in headlines. But this time it's his son making the news.

What you are about to read is truly amazing- or is it? Donald Trump Jr. was born in 1977. At some point during this decade, he will be able to say, "My father may lay claim to having his name spread all over creation, but I'm here today to tell you that I am one of very few people who can make this claim- I, Donald Trump Jr., was 37 years old two days ago. Next year, I will be 40."

How can The Donald's son accurately make that claim?

Rhyme Time

I can sizzle like bacon,
I am made with an egg,
I have plenty of backbone,
But lack a good leg.
I peel layers like onions,
But still remain whole,
I can be long like a flagpole,
Yet fit in a hole.
What am I?

Answer (Trump Teaser)

He, or anyone else who's born on December 31,
can fashion such a statement. In Junior's case,
he was born December 31, 1977. He can make that
claim on January 1, 2016.

Answer (Rhyme Time)

A snake

 *They can be made and they can
be laid. They can be bent and they
can be broken. But they cannot be
touched. What are they?*

Rules

HOLIDAY HUMDINGER

During Christmas, people produce
four million tons of waste resulting
from this alone.

Wrapping paper.

TIME AND TIME AGAIN

1. What is one-sixtieth of one-sixtieth of one-twenty-fourth of a day?

2. True or false: Any month that starts on a Sunday will have a Friday the 13th.

3. When is the only time (remember, we're talking time here) you can add five to eleven and have the solution be four?

4. If it were an hour later, it would be half as long 'til noon as it is now. If it were two hours earlier, it would be twice as long to noon as it is now. What time is it?

5. What word, when written in capital letters, is the same spelled backwards, forwards, and upside down?

VACATION VEXER

Anthony and Judy Salerno owned a pizzeria in the suburbs of Chicago. Years of hard work had enabled them to save up enough for the trip of a lifetime to see their long lost relatives who lived on the waters of Venice. At the same time, the couple had a tremendous fear of flying and boating there was out of the question. They finally settled on an acceptable means of transportation. What was it?

Answers (Time and Time Again)

1. One second

2. True

3. If you were to tack on five hours to eleven o'clock, the time would be four o'clock.

4. 10 a.m.

5. NOON

Answer (Vacation Vexer)

To take either a car or train to Venice, Florida

 Even if you give it to someone else, you still get to keep it. What is it?

Your word

HOLIDAY HUMDINGER

True or false? Two of Santa's reindeer, Donner and Blitzen, were originally called Dunder and Blixem.

True (as in the 1823 Christmas poem *A Visit from St. Nicholas*)

You 'Da Man!

See if you can solve these manly mindbogglers.

1. A man lives on the 20th floor of an apartment building. Every day he takes the elevator to the ground floor. When he returns, he takes it to the 10th floor and walks up the stairs to get to his apartment. Why?

2. A man went to a party, but stayed just briefly and only had a glass of punch. He was fortunate to be the first to drink it because everyone else who did died of poisoning. How come?

3. A man was bragging about his local softball team. He said, "Four of our men hit home runs and two of them were grand slams. We won 10 to 0 and not a single man crossed home plate." How could that be?

A Jenny-Craig Story

Jenny and Craig hadn't seen each other for years when they met at a class reunion. Craig ribbed his former classmate, "Geez, Jenny. You must have put on a hundred pounds!" Jenny laughed, even though Craig was correct- and even though she wasn't overweight. What's the story here?

Answers (You 'Da Man!)

1. He's not tall enough to reach the "20th floor" button so he presses number 10 and walks the remaining way.

2. Someone placed the poison in ice cubes. Because the man was an early-to-arrive and early-to-leave fellow, he drank the punch before the cubes melted.

3. They were all married.

Answer (A Jenny-Craig Story)

It was a kindergarten reunion.

 What goes up and never comes down?

Your age

HOLIDAY HUMDINGER

What Christmas song, written by Jay Livingston and Ray Evans, was introduced in the 1951 movie *The Lemon Drop Kid* starring Bob Hope?

Silver Bells

ALL IN THE FAMILY

1. A lawyer and doctor were standing on line at the supermarket. One of them was the father of the other's son. Can you explain?

2. Is it possible for a man to have been married to his widow's sister?

3. When you're describing a pair of twins, how many people are you talking about?

4. A man and his sister were walking in the park one day when the man pointed to a boy and said, "There's my nephew." His sister said, "That's right, but he's not my nephew." How come?

5. Michael has twice as many brothers as he has sisters. His sister Judy has five times as many brothers as she has sisters. How many brothers and sister are in the family?

6. Jennifer and Lori were born on the same day. They have the same parents. They are sisters - but they are not twins. How can this be?

7. The man married the little boy's mother, but was not his father (in any step of the way). Who was he?

8. Why would you doubt this young woman's story? "My mother dreamed that she was drowning and became so frightened that she died of a heart attack in her sleep."

Answers (All in the Family)

1. They were husband and wife.

2. Sure... If he married his wife's sister first.

3. Two... A twin is one person. A pair of twins is like a pair of shoes.

4. It was the woman's son so the boy was her brother's nephew.

5. There are five boys and two girls.

6. They are two of a set of triplets (or more).

7. The clergyman

8. No one would know what a dying woman was dreaming.

HOLIDAY HUMDINGER

If you were born on Christmas Day, what would your astrological sign be?

Capricorn

TRIVIQUATION

Test your math and your trivia wits here. Fill in the number portion of the answers suggested by the clues and then perform the arithmetic to solve the Triviquation.

1. Players on a lacrosse team   _____

2. White stripes on a U.S. flag   - _____

3. Strings on a violin   x _____

4. Letters in Greek alphabet   - _____

5. Times Ford was elected U.S. President   = _____

OLD GLORY

1. How many stripes did the U.S. flag have when Francis Scott Key wrote the Star Spangled Banner?

2. Destroying the American flag is frowned upon and is in some cases against the law, but what American hero was honored for doing so?
Hint: Think North Pole.

3. What do the terms "hoist" and "fly" refer to?

4. True or false? The flag's colors, red, white and blue, have no particular significance.

Answers (Triviquation)

1. 12

2. 6

3. 4

4. 24

5. 0

Answers (Old Glory)

1. 15, which represented the amount of states at that time

2. Robert Peary left pieces of the flag scattered at the North Pole.

3. The hoist is the attached side of the flag while the fly is the body of it.

4. False - Red stands for heartiness and valor; white symbolizes purity and innocence; and blue is for vigilance and perseverance.

HOLIDAY HUMDINGER

The Twelve Days of Christmas covers what period of time?

December 25 to January 5 (January 6th is the start of Epiphany.)

WHAT NEXT?

This game involves finding the common link of the series below and then filling in what should follow.

Example: J,F,M,A,M,J,J,A,S,O,N, D - for December, completing the series of the months of the year.

1. 6, 6, 7, 9, 8 , 6, ...?

2. A, K, Q, J, T, ...?

3. S.A., J.P., J.C., J.L., ...?

4. Alpha, Bravo, Charlie, Delta, ...?

5. A, P, A, T, G, C, L, V, L, S, S, ...?

RHYME TIME

Often talked of, never seen,
Ever coming, never been.
Daily looked for, never here,
Still approaching, coming near.
Though they expect me to appear,
They will never find me here.

What am I?

Answers (What Next?)

1. 8 - The number of letters in the days of the week beginning with Sunday.

2. N - The descending order of cards.

3. J.F. - Jimmy Fallon (major hosts of *The Tonight Show*)

4. Echo ... These are the first five letters of the phonetic alphabet.

5. C - Capricorn (signs of the zodiac).

Answer (Rhyme Time)

Tomorrow (or the future)

HOLIDAY HUMDINGER

If you suffered from pogonophobia, why might you be afraid of Santa Claus?

Pogonophobia is a fear of beards.

ALL WET

Santa "reigns" when it comes to water teasers.
Try your hand at these.

1. Penelope was found dead lying beside a puddle of water and broken glass. She had no cuts or bruises on her body. There was no sign of physical trauma. How did Penelope die?

2. David Copperelf is the premier magician here at the North Pole. One day, David exclaimed that he would walk across the surface of Lizard Lake without the aid of any equipment. He made good on his promise. How did he do it?

3. Our elfish magician was at it again with a water glass filled to the brim. He held the glass above his head and then let it drop to the floor without spilling a single drop of water. How did he manage to pull off this one?

4. Secretary Sally was making herself some coffee when the pendant her boss had given her for Christmas fell off her blouse and into the cup. The cup had coffee in it but the pendant didn't get wet. How come?

TABLE TALK

You put it on the table, cut it and then properly pass portions of it around the table, but you never eat it. What is it?

Answers (All Wet)

1. Penelope was a goldfish. Her bowl got knocked over and she suffocated.

2. Lizard Lake was frozen.

3. The glass was filled all right, but not with water.

4. It was instant coffee that hadn't been liquefied yet.

Answer (Table Talk)

A deck of cards

 What has a foot at each end and one in the middle?

A yardstick

HOLIDAY HUMDINGER

True or false? In Caracas, Venezuela, it is customary for people to roller-skate to church on Christmas Eve.

True

SPORTS SHORTS

Check out your sports smarts with these brain bafflers.

1. Quarterback Russell Wilson can hurl a football that would stop in mid-flight, reverse direction and then return to him. How does he manage this?

2. Is there better than a 50-50 chance that the next U.S. Tennis Open winner will have more than the average number of arms?

3. Football is doubly popular in this case. The Steelers and Eagles are two teams that have it; however, the Cowboys and Packers don't - and although the Lions had it first, the Bills have it twice. What is it?

4. A man left home one day and made three left turns. He then met a man wearing a mask. What was the first man's profession? And the second?

5. This one's a true story... A horse named Cilohocla once made the circuit at Florida race tracks. Can you come up with a spirited reason why the stud was so named?

PICTURE PURCHASE

An art aficionado bought a useless painting at a garage sale, but knew that he was getting a lot more than he paid for. How so?

Answers (Sports Shorts)

1. He throws it straight up into the air.

2. Of course ... Since the average number of arms on a human is slightly less than two, anyone with two arms has more than the average.

3. The letter "l."

4. The first man was a baseball player. So was the second man -a catcher.

5. Backwards, it spells "alcoholic."

Answer (Picture Purchase)

The frame around it was invaluable.

HOLIDAY HUMDINGER

Robert Louis Stevenson, author of Treasure Island, willed his November 13th birthday to a friend. Why?

Because she disliked her own Christmas birthday.

OPPOSITES ATTRACT

These opposites have attracted so much that they've combined and need to be unscrambled.

Example: EHTLIFRTG is RIGHT/LEFT.

1. NRRUODEVE

2. FDOHSTRA

3. GTLIBLEIT

4. NRCTDILEYA

5. NPWUOD

6. OEMCOG

7. MTOTPBTOO

8. CITLHBWEKA

9. VEOOBBWALE

10. LEPFTMYLU

LETTER PERFECT

Which of the following letter designs does not belong with the other six?   Y E N F A H Z

Answers (Opposites Attract)

1. UNDER/OVER

2. SOFT/HARD

3. BIG/LITTLE

4. CLEAN/DIRTY

5. UP/DOWN

6. COME/GO

7. TOP/BOTTOM

8. BLACK/WHITE

9. ABOVE/BELOW

10. FULL/EMPTY

Answer (Letter Perfect)

The letter E, which requires four perfectly straight lines-
All the others have three.

HOLIDAY HUMDINGER

What charitable organization revved
up its first Christmas toy drive for
needy youngsters in 1947?

Toys for Tots

CLUELESS

Disregarding any clues, you should be able to find below the only word in the English language that has four consecutive double letters.

SAUBNBOYOKCKLEUEEPSER

If you've gotten the drift, there's no need for further help here to find the only word with five consecutive vowels.

FUQRUETUHEERHIENLPG

Let's remove any doubt at this point. We think you know what's going on, so you should be able to find the longest word with only one vowel.

ASNTRYDENOGTUBHST

FORWARD THINKING

If we were across the pond and using the King's English, we might call this the 2,000 pound question. In the U.S.A. it would be, well, the 2,000 pound question.

Forward I'm heavy, backward I'm not. What am I?

Answers (Clueless)

If you deleted the words "any clues" as suggested, you'd be left with subbookkeeper.

Continuing with that premise, you didn't need "further help", so once those words were removed, queueing was left as the solution.

The longest word with only one vowel, strengths, became evident with the removal of "any doubt."

Answer (Forward Thinking)

A ton

What has to be broken before it can be used?

An egg

HOLIDAY HUMDINGER

What was the name of the 12-year-old boy who sang the hit tune, *I Saw Mommy Kissing Santa Claus?*

Jimmy Boyd

MIXED BAG

1. I live in a house in which all the windows on all four sides face south. How is that possible?

2. If a brick weighs three pounds plus half a brick, how much does a brick and a half weigh?

3. What common element is expressed in the following letters? **HIJKLMNO**

4. There are 6 pears in a basket and 6 people in the room. How can you give each person a pear and still leave a pear in the basket?

5. How long would it take to boil 3 three-minute eggs?

6. Can you name the oldest settler in the west?

7. What is it that every man, no matter how meticulous or clever, always overlooks?

8. What is taken before you get it?

9. What men are always above board in their movements?

10. Add these numbers in your noggin: Begin with 1000. Add 40. Now add another 1000. Add 30. Now add another 1000. Add 20. Now add another 1000. Add 10. and your answer is ...?

Answers (Mixed Bag)

1. The house is at the North Pole.

2. Nine pounds - The brick weighs six pounds and half a brick weighs in at three pounds.

3. H_2O

4. You give the last person the whole basket, pear included.

5. Three minutes

6. The sun

7. His nose

8. A picture

9. Chessmen

10. By any chance, did you get 5000? The correct answer is 4100.

HOLIDAY HUMDINGER

In what country is the Christmas gift-giver a kindly old witch named La Befana?

Italy

CONNECTIONS

Fill in the blanks and connect the words below.

Example: fishing _____ cat becomes fishing pole cat

1. Red _____ stitch

2. Chocolate _____ condition

3. Thin _____ breaker

4. Easter _____ salad

5. Rocking _____ shoe

6. Jumping _____ knife

7. Butter _____ tape

8. Chevy _____ Gogh

9. Electric _____ card

10. Spare _____ West

RHYME TIME

I may fall, but I never break.
Children I may cause to quake.
You lose energy as I come your way.
I'm part of your week,
But not your day.
What am I?

Answers (Connections)

1. Cross

2. Mint

3. Ice

4. Egg

5. Horse

6. Jack

7. Scotch

8. Van

9. Charge

10. Key

Answer (Rhyme Time)

Night

How the Grinch Stole Christmas was written by Theodor Geisel but you know him better by his pen name. What is it?

Dr. Seuss

CHAIN LETTERS

In these puzzles, you must turn the first word into
the second by changing one letter at a time
and forming a new word at each stage.

1. Make FIRE produce HEAT:
   FIRE - ___ - ___ - ___ - ___ - HEAT

2. Change MICE into RATS:
   MICE - ___ - ___ - ___ - RATS

3. Obtain LOAN from BANK:
   BANK - ___ - ___ - ___ - ___ - LOAN

4. Turn SLEEP into DREAM:
   SLEEP - ___ - ___ - ___ - ___ - ___ - DREAM

5. Turn TEARS into SMILE:
   TEARS - ___ - ___ - ___ - ___ - ___ - SMILE

6. Make DEAD be LIVE:
   DEAD - ___ - ___ - ___ - ___ - ___ - LIVE

7. Put MILK into PAIL:
   MILK - ___ - ___ - ___ - PAIL

8. Evolve FISH into BIRD:
   FISH - ___ - ___ - ___ - ___ - BIRD

9. Turn OIL into GAS:
   OIL - ___ - ___ - ___ - ___ - GAS

10. Turn MORE into LESS:
    MORE - ___ - ___ - ___ - LESS

Answers (Chain Letters)

1. FIRE - HIRE - HERE - HERD - HEAD - HEAT

2. MICE - MITE - MATE - MATS - RATS

3. BANK - BONK - BOOK - LOOK - LOON - LOAN

4. SLEEP - BLEEP - BLEED - BREED - BREAD - DREAD - DREAM

5. TEARS - SEARS - STARS - STARE - STALE - STILE - SMILE

6. DEAD - LEAD - LEND - LENT - LINT - LINE - LIVE

7. MILK - MILL - PILL - PALL - PAIL

8. FISH - FIST - GIST - GIRT - GIRD - BIRD

9. OIL - NIL - NIP - NAP - GAP - GAS

10. MORE - LORE - LOSE - LOSS - LESS

HOLIDAY HUMDINGER

What novelty song performed by Elmo and Patsy is a perennial holiday hit?

Grandma Got Run Over by a Reindeer

Junkyard Wars

Chopper and Louie worked at a junkyard and normally were the best of pals. Lately though, they had been getting on each other's nerves. Something had to give, and one day at lunch, it did.

Chopper, by far the larger of the two men, strode over to Louie and said, "Let's settle our differences with a bet. I bet you $100 that I can carry something in that wheelbarrow over there that you can't. Choose anything from the yard and push it. I say I can carry that and more."

Louie, who was built...well, like a guy named Louie, felt like he had to accept the bet and agreed.

"Anything you want, Louie," Chopper goaded him. "There's a Buick tranny over there, here's a stack of car batteries, an engine out of an '83 Ford. Grab anything you want for the wheelbarrow. You push it and I bet I can push it and a lot more."

What two words did Louie say to win the bet?

Back and Forth

Without switching their order, how can you make these numbers read like a palindrome- the same from left to right as right to left? **14351026987**

Answer (Junkyard Wars)

"Hop in."

Answer (Back and Forth)

Make them Roman Numerals- I IV III V X II VI IX VIII VII

How many bricks does it take to complete a building made of brick?

Just one- The last one.

Is the North Pole located in Alaska, Idaho, New York, Oklahoma or "all of the above"?

All of the above- There are four cities by that name in the U.S.

SANTA'S HELPERS

All the world has contributed to the magic of Christmas. For a heaping plate of Mrs. Claus' homemade Christmas cookies next time you are up here at the North Pole, see if you can match the following Christmas traditions with their place of origin.

1. Christmas trees   a) Mexico

2. The "X" in "Xmas"   b) Greece

3. Plum pudding   c) Russia

4. Kissing under the mistletoe   d) Denmark

5. Poinsettia flowers   e) Britain

6. Christmas seals   f) Scandinavia

7. The writer of *White Christmas*   g) Germany

MISS DAISY'S DRIVING

Daisy's car is parked on the street facing north. She gets in, takes off and drives along the street for a mile, winding up a mile south from her original starting point. What happened here?

Answers (Santa's Helpers)

1. G

2. B

3. E

4. F

5. A

6. D

7. C (Irving Berlin)

Answer (Miss Daisy's Driving)

She was driving in reverse.

HOLIDAY HUMDINGER

40% of the country of Sweden sits down on Christmas Eve to traditionally watch what Disney cartoon character?

Donald Duck

VOWEL PLAY

Following are some unique observations-
words to live by, and words completed by simply
filling in the vowels where applicable.

1. 'm nbdy, nbdy s prfct, nd thrfr 'm prfct.

2. Yr ftr dpnds n yr drms, s g t slp!

3. Bttr t rmn slnt nd b thght fl, thn t spk nd rmv ll dbt.

4. f clttrd dsk s sgn f clttrd mnd, thn n mpty dsk...

5. Clbcy sn't hrdtry.

6. 'v gt t st dwn nd wrk t whr stnd.

7. Whr thr's wll, wnt t b n t.

8. wst s trrbl thng t mnd.

9. Ppl wh snr lwys fll slp frst.

10. Th tm t nsr tht th tlt wrks s bfr y rlly nd t.

Answers (Vowel Play)

1. I'm a nobody, nobody is perfect, and therefore I'm perfect.

2. Your future depends on your dreams, so go to sleep!

3. Better to remain silent and be thought a fool, than to speak and remove all doubt.

4. If a cluttered desk is a sign of a cluttered mind, then an empty desk…(is a sign of an empty mind)

5. Celibacy isn't hereditary.

6. I've got to sit down and work out where I stand.

7. Where there's a will, I want to be in it.

8. A waist is a terrible thing to mind.

9. People who snore always fall asleep first.

10. The time to ensure that the toilet works is before you really need it.

HOLIDAY HUMDINGER

True or false: St. Francis of Assisi created the first nativity scene in the 13th century.

True

On A Very Special Episode of Survivor Island...

Contestants on the reality show Survivor Island were in a fix. Supplies were running dangerously low and most of the island was overrun with man-eating crabs. They needed to get across the shark-infested lagoon to a neighboring island with fresh stocks and an anti-crab electric fence. The problem was that Jack weighed 200 pounds, Mike weighed 140 pounds and Lori tipped the scales at exactly 100 pounds. The weight limit for their tiny dugout canoe was 250 pounds, so there was no way they could all fit.

Knowing that the crabs would be there by sundown, how did all three avoid starvation and/or becoming crab bait?

Chime Time

A man arrived home late one night. When he opened the door, he heard the clock chime once. A half hour later, it chimed once. The same thing happened another half hour later. And a half hour after that, the clock yet again chimed only once. If the clock chimes the number of times to indicate the hour, and then once on the half-hour, what time did the man arrive home?

Answer (Survivor Island)

Mike and Lori took the canoe to the new island.
Lori stayed at the new campsite while Mike paddled
back. When he arrived, he turned the canoe over
to Jack, who beat a hasty retreat to the new crab-proof
beach. Jack landed the boat with a thump, and as
he climbed ashore, Lori got back in the canoe to go
pick up Mike. That night, with full bellies, they slept
the sleep of the crabless.

Answer (Chime Time)

Midnight- He heard the last chime at twelve, one at
12:30, another at l:00 A.M. and one more at 1:30.

What gets whiter the dirtier it gets?

A chalkboard

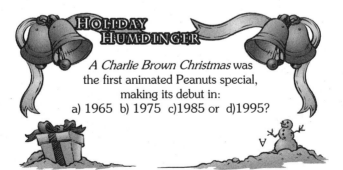

HOLIDAY HUMDINGER

A Charlie Brown Christmas was
the first animated Peanuts special,
making its debut in:
a) 1965 b) 1975 c)1985 or d)1995?

A

WHAT IS IT?

1. You can see me and you can feel me, but if you touch me, you will die.

2. You take away the outside and cook the inside. Then you eat the outside and throw away the inside.

3. I come at night without being called, and am lost in the day without being stolen.

4. I get bigger the more you take away from me.

5. Keep me whole and I can be anyone. Break me to pieces and I am no one.

6. The more I dry, the wetter I get.

7. I have a neck, but no head and two arms, but no hands.

8. I start with the letter E. I end with the letter E. I usually have only one letter, but I am not the letter E!

9. What seven-letter word becomes longer when you remove its third letter?

10. What's made by light and yet does not contain any light?

Answers (What Is It?)

1. The sun

2. An ear of corn

3. A star

4. A hole

5. A mirror

6. A towel

7. A shirt

8. An envelope

9. Lounger

10. A shadow

HOLIDAY HUMDINGER

True or false: The first song
ever broadcast from space was *Jingle Bells,*
sung by astronauts Wally Schirra and
Tom Stafford while aboard Gemini 6 on
December 16, 1965.

True